Con

e

I

Introduction

It would be a rare primary teacher who said that they had time to spare; but even in the busiest day there may be a few minutes left after the work has been done and everything is packed away. This is the perfect opportunity to carry out a quick science demonstration that will fire children's imaginations.

The activities in this book are intended for teacher demonstration, but, wherever possible and safe, children should be involved in the practical aspects of the activity. Learning for all children will be enhanced by the opportunity to participate, even if their experience is vicarious. However, when allowing children to participate in activities involving food be aware of allergies or other dietary conditions such as diabetes.

It is not essential that children come up with the 'correct' scientific explanations, many of which lie outside the KS2 programme of study. Rather, the main point of all these demonstrations is to get them discussing ideas with each other and the teacher, as well as using reasoned arguments to predict and explain the outcome of the activities.

With this in mind, it is important not to give away the right answer too soon as this will stop the discussion. Many teachers may even choose not to give the scientific explanation at all, preferring to leave their pupils curious. This may stimulate many pupils to continue the discussions outside the classroom or to undertake some research for themselves.

Finally, most *Six Minute Science* can be done with very little preparation, but it is advisable to try the activities out yourself before showing them to the class so that you are comfortable with what to do and what to expect, ensuring the best results.

How to use Six Minute Science

Each activity is organised under the following headings:

What you need: Tells you exactly what you need for the activity.

What you do: Tells you what to prepare and what to do in the classroom, and sometimes suggests what to ask (in italics).

What happens: Describes the results you should get.

Why it happens: Explains, in simple scientific terms, why you should get those results.

By the way: Gives extra information, including extension activities and safety issues where necessary.

     This sign indicates that the activity must be carried out by an adult or under adult supervision due to the use of heat, sharp objects, etc.

Curriculum links: The references at the bottom of each activity provide a link to the National Curriculum for England and the QCA Schemes of Work. In addition to the references given, these activities all relate to the KS2 Sc1 Scientific Enquiry section. There are also links to the National Guidelines for Environmental Studies in Scotland, a key for which is provided on p.48.

We wish you many an enjoyable and thought provoking 'Six Minutes'!

Measure your reaction time

How quickly can the children catch a falling ruler? The scale on the ruler gives their results.

In the classroom

What you need

A 30 cm ruler.

What you do

Ask for a volunteer. They stand in front of you with their hands a little apart, palms facing inwards.
Hold the ruler, by the 30 cm end, between your fingers and thumb so that the tip of it hangs between the child's hands.
Tell them that you are going to let go of the ruler and that they must catch it.
Without warning, let it go.

What happens

As soon as the ruler falls, the volunteer brings their palms together to catch it. You look at the number on the ruler that shows just above their palms. This is a measure of the child's reaction time. The further the ruler falls through the hands of the child before they catch it, the slower their reaction time.

Background Information

Why it happens

The volunteer's eyes tell their brain that the ruler is falling and their brain tells their hands to catch it. The slower the messages to and from the brain, the slower their reaction time.

By the way

Reaction times get faster with practice so children should do better on average after a few attempts.

Ask the class when they think fast reactions are useful, for example when catching a ball or getting a quick start to a race when "Go" is called.

There are a number of reaction time computer programs available, which will give more accurate readings.

Curriculum links

KS2 Sc2 2e. QCA SoW 5A Keeping healthy
Health Ed/TRH/PH/Level D/Target 1,4

How sensitive are you?

Demonstrate that different parts of our body have different degrees of sensitivity.

In the classroom

What you need

A bent hairpin or a Kirby grip with two blunt ends.

What you do

Explain that different parts of our bodies vary in sensitivity.
Which areas do you think would be most sensitive?
Ask a volunteer to close their eyes.
Touch the fingertips of your volunteer with either one or two ends of the hair grip, making sure the class can see how many ends you are using.
Ask the volunteer how many ends they can feel.
Now try less sensitive parts of the body such as an arm, a leg or the back of the shoulder.

What happens

On the more sensitive parts of the body, e.g. fingertips and lips, it is possible to tell whether one or both ends of the hairpin are touching, but this is not possible on the less sensitive parts, e.g. legs and the back of the shoulder. In fact, even if you pull the points quite far apart it is almost impossible to tell one end from two on the shoulder.

Background Information

Why it happens

Different parts of the body don't all need the same level of sensitivity to function properly. It is clearly useful to have very sensitive fingertips because we use them to touch and feel different textures, temperatures, and to pick things up etc, but it is less useful to have sensitive skin on your legs or shoulders.

We are sensitive because of the nerve endings just under the skin. The nerves carry impulses from the nerve endings to the brain where they are analysed. The more nerve endings there are, the more sensitive that part of the body is and the more information the brain will receive.

By the way

 Warn the children that a touch with the grip ends is enough and show them the blunt ends of the grip – you don't want them sticking pins in each other!

Curriculum links

KS2 Sc2 2e. QCA SoW 4A Moving and growing, 5A Keeping healthy
Health Ed/TRH/PH/Level D/Target 1

How long is your gut?

Show the children just how long their intestine is.

In the Classroom

What you need

A large box (to represent the abdomen) and around 6m of hosepipe (to represent the intestine).

What you do

Before the lesson, coil the pipe into the box and close it.
Which parts of the digestive system can you name?
Show the class the box and explain that it is like their abdomen.
Make sure they realise that the abdomen is the area from below their ribcage to the top of their legs.
Then reveal the end of the hosepipe.
Ask a volunteer to pull the pipe slowly out of the box.

What happens

The intestine, when completely uncoiled, stretches to the back of the room.

Background Information

Why it happens

The intestine is the place where food is broken down (digested) and absorbed into the body. This is a slow process and so the intestine needs to be very long to give the body time to digest all the food. Because it is so long, the intestine has to be coiled up tightly to fit inside the body!

By the way

This activity demonstrates the length of the 'small' intestine. The whole intestine is actually in two parts: the 6m long small intestine and the 1.5m long large intestine.

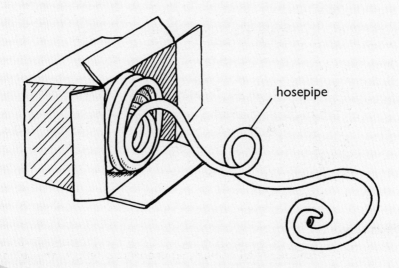

hosepipe

Curriculum links

KS2 Sc2 2b. QCA SoW 5A Keeping healthy
Health Ed/TRH/PH/Level D/Target 1

unit 5A Digesting a banana sandwich

Turn a banana sandwich into a disgusting mush to demonstrate what happens when food is digested.

In the classroom

What you need

An apron, a table knife, a banana sandwich, a potato masher, a cup of water, a really strong plastic bag, red and green food colouring, some vinegar, some washing-up liquid, a sieve and a large bowl.

What you do

Cover the table, put on the apron and tell the children that you are going to show them what happens to food in your gut.
Cut up the sandwich. *This represents the incisors cutting the food.*
Use the potato masher to grind up the sandwich. *This represents the molars grinding the food.*
Add water and a little red food colouring. *The water is the saliva and the food colour represents the enzymes in the saliva getting to work.*
Scoop into the plastic bag with some green food colouring. *The bag represents the stomach and the food colour is the bile from the liver.*
Add some vinegar. *This represents the acids in the stomach.*
Give it all a good squeeze. *This shows the stomach muscles at work.*
Then add some washing-up liquid. *Chemicals called enzymes make it possible to digest food – as well as producing embarrassing gases!*
Sieve the whole mess into a large bowl.

What happens

The sandwich is transformed into a paste.

Background Information

Why it happens

The body needs to break food down into simple particles (molecules) that can be used to provide the energy and nutrients it needs to function. It cannot draw out and absorb the components of food without mushing it together and bathing it in digestive chemicals called enzymes.

By the way

Chewing food thoroughly is important. It needs to be well mixed with saliva to slide down easily and start being digested.
Children who have vomited will remember the acidic taste. This is because of the acids in the stomach.

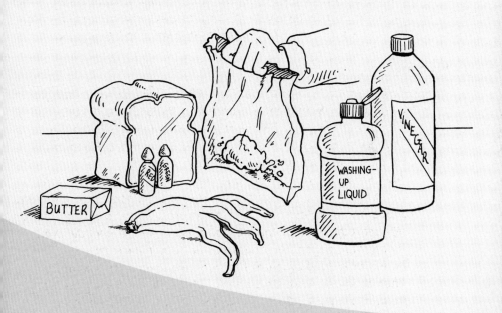

Curriculum links

KS2 Sc2 2a,b. QCA SoW 3A Teeth and eating, 5A Keeping healthy
Health Ed/TRH/PH/Level D/Target 1

Explosive dispersal

Use a balloon and some confetti to show how some plant seeds are dispersed by explosion.

In the classroom

What you need

The 'confetti' from a hole punch, a balloon, an old sheet and a pin.

What you do

Shake the 'confetti' into the mouth of the balloon using a rolled up paper funnel.
Blow up the balloon and tie off.
Cover the floor with the sheet.
How are seeds dispersed?
Tell the class that you are going to demonstrate how some kinds of seeds can be dispersed by explosion.
Point out that the balloon is acting as a seedcase, and the paper inside is the seeds.
Hold the balloon over the sheet and burst it!

What happens

The confetti seeds fly everywhere.

Background Information

Why it happens

When the balloon (the seed pod) pops, the air pressure released carries the confetti (seeds) with it, scattering it. The purpose of seed dispersal is to spread the plants widely and to reduce competition between the growing plant and its parent.

By the way

Lupin seeds are dispersed by explosion. Refer back to other methods of dispersal, for example, by floating on water (coconut), by wind (sycamore) or by clinging to animals (burdock).
Ask the children to think of ways of modelling other dispersal mechanisms. For example, paper floating on water models water-borne seeds and paper spinners model wind-borne seeds. Velcro models plant burrs – indeed, plant burrs were the inspiration for Velcro's invention!

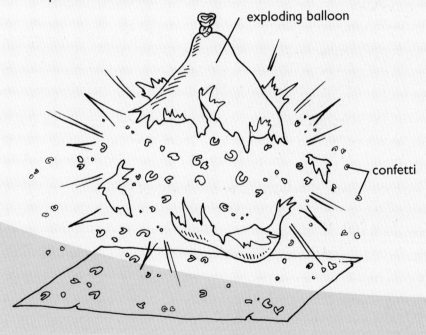

exploding balloon

confetti

Curriculum links

KS2 Sc2 3d. QCA SoW 5B Life cycles
Envtl St/Science/LT&PL/PL/Level D/Target 5

The pollination game

Use role play to demonstrate how flowers are pollinated by insects.

In the classroom

What you need

Some sticky balls made with Velcro, a couple of really woolly jumpers and two cartons of fruit juice with straws.

What you do

Ask for three volunteers. One holds a drink carton and the Velcro balls, representing a beautiful flower bearing nectar and pollen. The other two put on the jumpers with one taking the second drink carton. The child without the drink is a bee, the other is a second beautiful flower. The children all stand about a metre apart.

Direct the children to enact the following story:

The first flower holds out their nectar and looks as beautiful as possible. The bee buzzes around until they spot the flower and its sweet nectar. The bee crosses to the flower and takes a sip of nectar. As the bee drinks, the flower sticks a couple of pollen grains to the bee's coat. Off the bee goes with the pollen. It spots the other flower, fancies more nectar and delivers the pollen.

What happens

The bee picks up and deposits the pollen from one flower to another as it visits them for the nectar.

Background Information

Why it happens

Pollination is the transmission of pollen from the anther to the stigma of flowers, after which fertilization can take place. Flowers cannot move and so they need to use other means to spread their pollen around. In insect pollination, plants 'bribe' insects to visit them by offering them nectar. Pollen grains from the anther of the plant are picked up on the legs and bodies of visiting insects and carried to the stigmas of other flowers for fertilization.

By the way

Wind pollination is literally more hit-and-miss. You can model it by having one 'flower' pelt the other with Velcro balls. Not many will stick. Point out that this is why wind-pollinated flowers produce so much pollen and have such long stigmas to catch it!

Curriculum links

KS2 Sc2 2d. QCA SoW 5B Life cycles
Envtl St/Science/LT&PL/PL/Level D/Target 5

unit 5c Why do the shapes move?

Demonstrate how the hot air rising from a radiator or candle can make hanging shapes spin.

In the classroom

What you need

Some aluminium cooking foil and string. If the classroom radiator is not on you will also need a candle and matches.

What you do

Cut some shapes, e.g. spirals, out of the cooking foil and bend them in various ways.
Hang the shapes over the hot radiator, or a lit candle.
Observe what happens.

What happens

The shapes start to spin.

Background Information

Why it happens

The air above the radiator is being heated up and is rising. Hot air rises because it is less dense than cold air. As it rises, the hot air pushes the foil shapes and makes them turn.

By the way

Loops, spirals and curves work best, offering shapes that can be easily turned by the rising air.

Talk about birds or hangliders using columns of hot air (risers) to hover above the earth without using any effort.

Also discuss candle-driven Christmas decorations like 'angel chimes'.

 If using a candle rather than a radiator take care that the shapes do not catch fire.

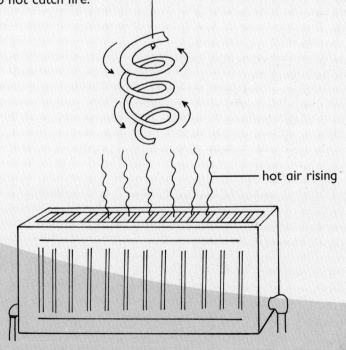

hot air rising

Curriculum links

KS2 Sc3 2b. QCA SoW 5C Gases around us
Envtl St/Science/E&F/PUE/Level E/Target 1

fire extinguisher!

A floating candle is extinguished by carbon dioxide gas.

In the classroom

What you need

A nightlight candle, a large jam jar, some water, some bicarbonate of soda, some vinegar, a match and a long splint.

What you do

Float the nightlight candle in a little water at the bottom of a large jam jar.
Light the candle with a long splint.
Can we put out the flame without blowing on it, dousing it with water or putting the lid on the jar?
Put several spoonfuls of bicarbonate of soda in the jar, adding it carefully to the water and avoiding the candle.
Then, carefully, without dousing the flame, add a little vinegar to the water/bicarbonate mix.
Ask the children to watch and explain what happens.

What happens

The mixture fizzes and the candle goes out.

Background Information

Why it happens

Fire needs oxygen to burn. Air contains oxygen, so the candle burns. The bicarbonate/vinegar mixture produces carbon dioxide (CO_2), a non-flammable gas. CO_2 is heavier than air so it pushes the air up and out. Without the oxygen, the candle cannot burn and so it goes out.

By the way

This is how carbon dioxide extinguishers put out a fire. The carbon dioxide smothers the flames and puts them out by stopping oxygen getting to them.

 Be careful that children do not inhale the bicarbonate of soda, or rub it in their eyes and take care when working with fire.

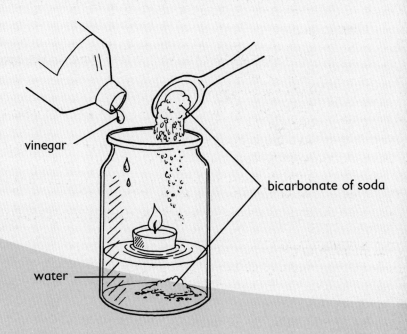

vinegar

bicarbonate of soda

water

Curriculum links

KS2 Sc3 2f. QCA SoW 5C Gases around us, 5D Changing state
Envtl St/Science/E&S/CM/Level E/Target 1

Is air real?

It's hard to believe that we live in 'an ocean of air', but this activity shows that although air is invisible, it is real.

In the Classroom

What you need

A paper towel, a clear plastic cup and a plastic aquarium full of water.

What you do

Is there a way to put the paper towel in the water without it getting wet?
Take a paper towel and crumple it up.
Push it to the bottom of clear plastic cup so that it gets lodged there.
Turn the cup upside down and plunge it into the water.
Lift the cup back out of the water and allow the children to feel the paper towel.

What happens

The paper towel stays dry.

Background Information

Why it happens

Pushing the cup into the water upside down traps the air inside it. As the cup is full of air, there is no way that the water can enter the cup so the paper towel stays dry.

By the way

Do the same again but this time turn the cup the right way up again. The air is lost and the towel gets wet!

Use two cups, one full of air and the other full of water, to 'pour' air, upside down, from one to the other, under the surface of the water.

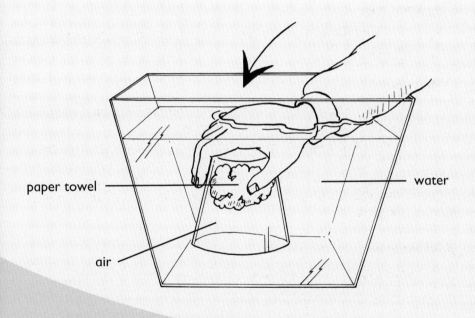

paper towel
water
air

Curriculum links

KS2 Sc3 1e. QCA SoW 5C Gases around us
Envtl St/Science/E&S/ME/Level C/Target 1

The Collapsing pop bottle

A bottle collapses without being touched – thanks to a little preparation and some air pressure!

In the Classroom

What you need

Some very hot water and an empty, screw-topped plastic pop bottle.

What you do

Choose a quiet time when the children are writing or otherwise occupied.
Pour a small amount of very hot water into the plastic bottle.
Swirl it round, pour it out, put it on your desk and screw the lid on tightly.
If necessary, draw the children's attention to the bottle.
What happens to the bottle?

What happens

Once the lid is screwed on tightly, there is a loud creaking and cracking as the bottle collapses.

Background Information

Why it happens

Heating the bottle with hot water expands the air inside and pushes some air out. Closing the lid tightly means that as the hot air cools and contracts, no new air can enter. As a result, the air pressure outside the bottle pushes the sides of the bottle in.

By the way

Have you ever had a shower and the shower curtain has blown inwards even though the window was closed and there was no draught? The differences in air pressure between the hot, expanded air inside the shower and the colder air outside the shower moves the curtain. Changes in air pressure also have an effect in nature. The heat of the Sun varies in intensity across the Earth. In some places it leads to high air pressure, in others it leads to low pressure. Air rushes from the high-pressure areas to the low, resulting in winds and weather.

 Take care when pouring the hot water into the bottle.

air

air
pressure

Curriculum links

KS2 Sc3 2d,e. QCA SoW 5C Gases around us
Envtl St/Science/E&S/ME/Level C/Target 1

The rain cycle in a bag

Show the whole rain cycle taking place in a sandwich bag on your window.

In the Classroom

What you need

A little water, a transparent sandwich bag and some clear sticky tape.

What you do

Choose a sunny window.
Pour a little water into the bottom of the bag.
Fold the top of the bag over several times to seal it.
Tape the top of the bag to the window.
Leave the bag for a couple of hours.
When ready to talk about the activity, tell the class that you think that it is looking cloudy somewhere in the room.
Draw their attention to the plastic bag.

What happens

A 'cloud' forms in the bag, although some water remains in the bottom. In effect, 'rain' is forming at the top of the bag. Occasionally, it drips and collects again at the bottom.

Background Information

Why it happens

The heat from the Sun causes some of the water in the bag to evaporate. The evaporated water forms a cloud of water vapour in the bag. Some water vapour then condenses on the bag. When a drop has reached a certain size, it *precipitates* – that is, it drips. It's raining!

By the way

Make sure it is a really sunny day or the water won't evaporate and form a cloud.

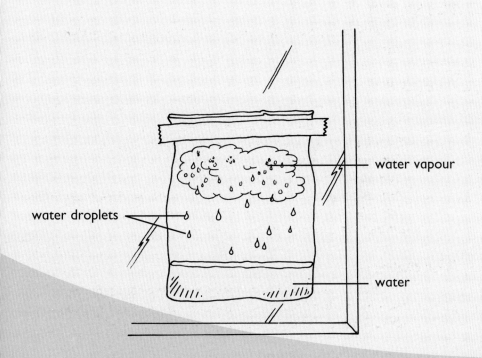

Curriculum links

KS2 Sc3 2e. QCA SoW 5D Changing state
Envtl St/Science/E&S/CM/Level C/Target 4

Melting icebergs

With a little preparation the day before, you can show that water moves as its temperature changes.

In the classroom

What you need

Some pre-prepared ice cubes with a little added food colouring. (Note that water with food colouring added takes longer to freeze.) You will also need a plastic pop bottle and some warm water.

What you do

Cut the top off the plastic bottle – to make it easy to insert the ice cube – and fill it with warm water.
Drop one of the coloured ice cubes into the warm water.
Invite the children to observe what happens.

What happens

The coloured ice cube floats on the surface and begins to melt. The food colouring makes the melted ice (water) visible as it sinks through the warm water. When it reaches the bottom of the bottle, it rises again, leaving behind a 'J' or 'U' shape the colour of the ice cube.

Background Information

Why it happens

As the ice melts, it turns into water. Because this water is cooler than the warm water, it is more dense and so heavier. As a result, the coloured water sinks. But as it sinks, it warms up, becomes less dense and so rises again.

By the way

Make sure the children understand that ice floats on water. Ice has a fixed solid structure that makes it less dense than water. As the ice cube continues to melt, amazing patterns, the colour of the ice cube, fill the bottle.

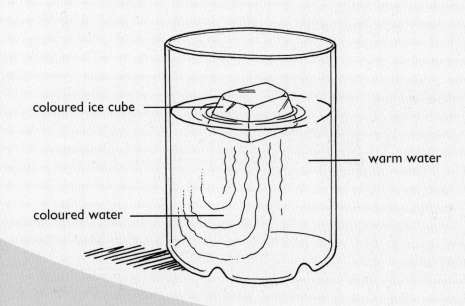

coloured ice cube

warm water

coloured water

Curriculum links

KS2 Sc3 2b. QCA SoW 5D Changing state
Envtl St/Science/E&S/CM/Level C/Target 4

unit 5D Making soft plastic

Make weak plastic strands, similar to the strands made in plastic manufacturing, using vinegar and milk.

In the classroom

What you need

A glass beaker, a bottle of vinegar (spirit vinegar is best because it is colourless), full-cream milk, a plastic pipette and a fine sieve or cheesecloth.

What you do

What do you know about plastic?
Fill the beaker with vinegar and hold it up.
Squirt some full-cream milk into it from the pipette.
Sieve the resulting mixture using the sieve or cheesecloth.

What happens

You make curious plastic fibres that are quite different from their constituent materials. The strands that are created have no great strength and can be easily shaped or moulded.

Background Information

Why it happens

The milk reacts with the vinegar, producing a simple 'plastic' material. The material is a protein from the milk called casein. It is separated out from the milk by the vinegar, which is a weak acid.

By the way

Casein is still used commercially in glues, cosmetics and to put a shiny surface on some papers.

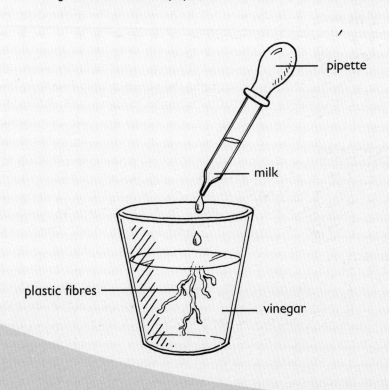

pipette

milk

plastic fibres

vinegar

Curriculum links

KS2 Sc3 2f. QCA SoW 5D Changing state, 6D Reversible and irreversible changes
Envtl St/Science/E&S/CM/Level C/Target 1

unit 5D An erupting volcano!

Make a live volcano using the chemical reaction between two common kitchen products.

In the classroom

What you need

A piece of board (a clay board is fine), a small plastic pop bottle, Plasticine or clay, bicarbonate of soda, some red food colouring and some vinegar.

What you do

What do volcanoes do?
Put the bottle in the middle of the board.
Build around it with Plasticine or clay so that the bottle mouth becomes the mouth of the volcano.
Put a spoonful of bicarbonate of soda in the bottle.
Add a few drops of red food colour – now the volcano is ready for action.
Cover the table in case of spills as the red food colour can spread and stain.
Keeping everyone at a safe distance and pour a little vinegar into the bottle.

What happens

The result will be an eruption of foaming red magma that pours satisfactorily from the bottle top.

Background Information

Why it happens

Vinegar – a weak acid – reacts with the bicarbonate of soda to produce carbon dioxide gas. This gas quickly fills the bottle, bubbling up and pushing the mixture out of the bottle top. The red food colour simply makes it look more like lava.

By the way

Make sure the bottle used is fairly small or the eruption will not occur.
Remind the children about lava – the igneous rock that emerges from inside the Earth.

 Be careful that children do not inhale the bicarbonate of soda, or rub it in their eyes.

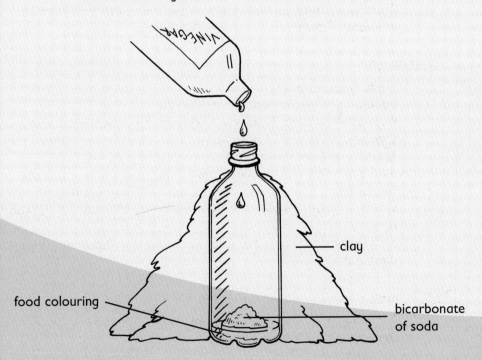

clay

food colouring

bicarbonate of soda

Curriculum links

KS2 Sc3 2f. QCA SoW 5D Changing state, 6D Reversible and irreversible changes
Envtl St/Science/E&S/CM/Level E/Target 1

unit 5D The floating canister

A carefully prepared film canister sinks, then surfaces as a result of the gas created by a chemical reaction.

In the Classroom

What you need

An empty film canister with a few small holes in the lid, a light weight such as a key, some string, a plastic aquarium filled with water and an effervescent indigestion tablet.

What you do

Tie the weight to the canister.
Show the children the canister and weight.
Put some water and an effervescent indigestion tablet in the film canister and put the lid back on.
Immediately put the canister into the plastic aquarium full of water so that the weight pulls it towards the bottom.
Ask the children to watch carefully and describe what happens.

What happens

After a few moments, the canister rises to the surface, pulling the weight with it.

Background Information

Why it happens

At first the canister sinks under the weight of the key. When the water reacts with the effervescent indigestion tablet it produces carbon dioxide gas. The gas replaces the water inside the canister causing the water to escape through the holes you made. As a result, the canister becomes lighter, and so up it rises!

By the way

Test this experiment out before showing it to the class to ensure that the weight used is heavy enough to sink the canister but light enough to let it rise once the reaction has taken place.

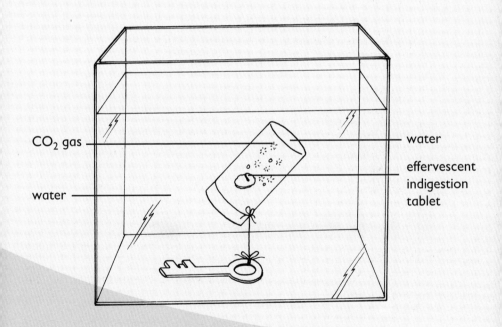

CO_2 gas

water

water

effervescent indigestion tablet

Curriculum links

KS2 Sc3 2f. QCA SoW 5D Changing state, 6D Reversible and irreversible changes
Envtl St/Science/E&S/CM/Level E/Target 1

unit 5D The Candle see-saw

Candle wax changes from solid to liquid which then drips, causing the candle to rock like a see-saw as it burns.

In the classroom

What you need

A long candle with a wick at both ends, a long nail, two drinking glasses, two saucers and a match.

What you do

Force the nail through the exact centre of the candle.
Balance the candle by the nail, between the two drinking glasses.
Put a saucer under each wick to catch the drips.
Light both wicks and observe what happens.

What happens

Both wicks burn. Wax drops from one end first and that end rises. Then the other end loses a drop of wax and rises while the first end drips again. The process of alternate drops of wax falling continues, and so the candle rocks back and forth.

Background Information

Why it happens

The solid wax fuel becomes liquid and burns. Some fuel is lost as gas (carbon dioxide) and some as water – both products of burning wax. Liquid fuel is also lost from each end in turn, changing the balance of the candle. The light end rises, the heavy end falls and so the candle rocks.

By the way

When wax burns, it produces carbon dioxide and water, and these are lost into the atmosphere. *But what about the liquid wax that runs down a burning candle? Does that still burn?*

 Take care when working with fire.

Curriculum links

KS2 Sc3 2g. QCA SoW 5C Gases around us, 5D Changing state
Envtl St/Science/E&S/CM/Level D/Target 1

Which force prevails?

Swirling a table tennis ball in a jar keeps it up when you might expect gravity to pull it down.

In the classroom

What you need

A table tennis ball and a large transparent jar.

What you do

Put the table tennis ball in the jar.
Place your hand over the opening of the jar and invert the jar.
Begin to swirl the jar round and round.
Take your hand away.

What happens

The ball climbs the walls of the jar and swirls around without falling back down.

Background Information

Why it happens

The ball is pushed outward by *centrifugal force* – a force that acts on objects flying outwards in a circle. The outward push on the walls of the jar stops the ball from dropping.

By the way

If you're brave, you could demonstrate the same force outside by swirling a bucket, half filled with water, by its handle. Make sure that all observers are standing well clear.

Some children might have tried the 'wall of death' or 'sticky fly' fairground ride in which the riders stand with their backs against the wall of a fast-rotating cylinder as the floor drops away. The riders stay 'stuck' to the wall.

There are also forces in nature that act like this; for example, the forces that hold our planet in orbit round the Sun, and the Moon in orbit round the Earth.

Curriculum links

KS2 Sc4 2b. QCA SoW 5E Earth, Sun and Moon, 6E Forces in action
Envtl St/Science/E&F/FTE/Level D/Target 2/Level E/Target I

Placing planets

Show the children just how big the solar system really is!

In the classroom

What you need

Two rolls of toilet paper and eleven name cards (Sun, Mercury, Venus, Earth, Mars, The Asteroid Belt, Jupiter, Saturn, Uranus, Neptune, Pluto).

What you do

You may need to work outside or in a very long corridor.

Explain to the class that they are going to help you model the solar system, to scale.

Start to unroll the toilet roll onto the floor and ask a child to stand on the very end – he or she is the Sun.

Unroll the paper and ask a child to stand at the fourth square holding the Mercury card.

Continue unrolling the paper, leaving a child and a name card at the following sheets: Venus sheet 7, Earth 10, Mars 15, The Asteroid Belt 28, Jupiter 52, Saturn 95, Uranus 192, Neptune 301 and Pluto 395.

What happens

The children end up standing very far apart, indicating just how impressive the distances in the solar system are.

Background Information

Why it happens

Planets revolve around the Sun in fixed orbits that are a particular distance from the Sun. These distances are determined by the forces of gravity that the Sun and the planets exert on each other.

By the way

You can develop the activity further by asking the children to hold various round objects to represent the planet whose name card they are holding. They are roughly in scale with each other, but not necessarily with the loo roll. Use: a beachball for the Sun, a small grape for Mercury, a large grape or strawberry for Venus, a large grape or strawberry for Earth, a cherry for Mars, round seeds for The Asteroid Belt, a watermelon for Jupiter, a melon for Saturn, a grapefruit for Uranus, a large orange for Neptune and a blackcurrant for Pluto.

Curriculum links

KS2 Sc4 4a,d. QCA SoW 5E Earth, Sun and Moon
Envtl St/Science/E&S/ES/Level C/Target 1

In orbit

Show how far away the Earth, the Sun and the Moon are from each other.

In the classroom

What you need

A marble, a dried pea or a peppercorn, and a beachball.

What you do

Take the class out into the playground.
Ask one child to stand in the middle of the playground holding the beachball. They are the Sun.
Take the rest of the class to the edge of the playground.
Give the marble to a child. They are the Earth.
Ask them to orbit the Sun by walking round it along the edge of the playground. They should be walking anticlockwise!
Complicate things by asking that they rotate as they orbit.
Give the pea or peppercorn to a child. They are the Moon.
Set the Moon in orbit round the Earth – anticlockwise again and this time always facing the Earth.
Set the Earth in orbit again, too!

What happens

The children demonstrate the orbits of the Earth and Moon around the Sun, gaining an idea of the relative distance of these heavenly bodies from each other – in as much as it is pretty impossible to imagine!

Background Information

Why it happens

These are the relative movements of these three masses, to a very approximate scale, showing that the Earth orbits anticlockwise round the Sun and that the Moon orbits anticlockwise round the Earth (hence also orbiting the Sun). They are held in their places by the gravitational force exerted by the Sun and by each other.

By the way

This is an opportunity to explain why eclipses are so rare. When the distances are this great, the chances of all three planets lining up are very unlikely.
The distances in this activity will only be roughly right. A million Earths would fit inside the Sun.
If the beachball is the Sun and therefore a star, where is the next star going to be? The answer is not the next street, or even the next town but the other side of the Atlantic.

Curriculum links

KS2 Sc4 4a,b,c,d. QCA SoW 5E Earth, Sun and Moon
Envtl St/Science/E&S/ES/Level C/Target 1

unit 5E Eating against gravity

A child tries to eat and drink upside down.

In the classroom

What you need

A plastic cup full of water, a plastic drinking bottle and a slice of bread. You will need to work in the gym, using a secure piece of apparatus with a horizontal bar.

What you do

Do you need gravity to take the food you eat to your stomach?
Ask a volunteer to hang upside down by their knees from the gym bar.
Give the volunteer a little bread to eat.
Then hand them a cup of water to drink. Beware of spills!
Lastly, give them the water bottle to drink from.
Ask the child to describe their experience to the class.

What happens

It feels strange, but eating and drinking are possible upside down and so the volunteer should have managed to eat some food and drink some water. The cup would have been tough, but a squeezy bottle makes it easier to drink without spills.

Background Information

Why it happens

Gravity is working in the reverse direction when you hang upside down. However, food travels via your gullet or *oesophagus* to your stomach in muscular waves – a bit like a worm moving – and so it can move through your body against, or even without, gravity.

By the way

What other bodily functions may be influenced by gravity?
Astronauts in space find that because their blood is still being pumped 'up' to their head but there is no pull down from gravity, their faces swell. After some time, however, their bodies adapt to the new conditions and their hearts beat around ten times a minute slower.

 Take care that the child doesn't choke or fall and only give them very small amounts of the bread.

Curriculum links

KS2 Sc4 2b. QCA SoW 5E Earth, Sun and Moon
Envtl St/Science/E&S/ES/Level D/Target 1

(unit 5F) Seeing an echo

Use the surface of water to model sound waves and show how an echo is formed

In the classroom

What you need

A washing-up bowl partly filled with water, a marble and a strip of something waterproof that you can curve, such as a plastic ruler.

What you do

Show the children the washing-up bowl partly filled with water. Drop a marble into the middle of the water and let the children see the ripples spread.

Then remove the marble and insert a curved plastic ruler between the walls of the bowl, ensuring that it is half above and half below the water surface. Drop the marble in again and observe what happens.

What happens

The ripples from the marble are obstructed by the plastic ruler and so they bounce off it in the reverse direction.

Background Information

Why it happens

The ripples are like sound waves in that they travel out from the source (though sound waves are emitted in all directions and not just out in horizontal circles). When they encounter a hard surface – the ruler – they bounce back. This is how echoes are made.

By the way

Many animals use echoes to help them find their way – bats and dolphins, for example. They make high pitched sounds that get echoed back to them, warning them of obstacles in their way. Fishing boats also use echo-sounding equipment to locate shoals of fish.

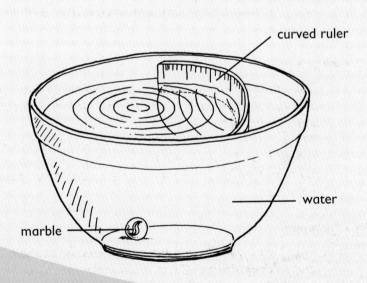

curved ruler

water

marble

Curriculum links

KS2 Sc4 3e,g. QCA SoW 5F Changing sounds
Envtl St/Science/E&F/PUE/Level E/Target 5

unit 5F Sound effects

Make a candle flame quiver by flicking a yoghurt pot to create sound waves.

In the classroom

What you need

A candle, a small metal tray or saucer, some sand, an empty yoghurt pot, some stiff paper, glue or an elastic band, and a match.

What you do

Make a yoghurt pot drum by covering the mouth of a yoghurt pot with stiff paper either by gluing it or gripping it tightly with an elastic band.

Cut a 1 cm hole in the centre of this paper drumskin.

Support the candle in sand on a metal tray in a draught-proof area and light it.

Point the yoghurt pot drum at the candle, drumskin away from you, and flick the base.

The children will be surprised at the volume. Those nearest the drum will hear it best.

What happens

The candle flame will quiver when the drum is flicked.

Background Information

Why it happens

The yoghurt pot concentrates the sound. It also focuses all the sound in one direction. The sound is carried to the candle through the air as waves. The candle is burning in air, and when the sound wave reaches it, the change in air pressure makes the candle quiver.

By the way

The sound from the yoghurt pot changes the air pressure, unlike blowing which simply makes the air move. As a result, the air quivers or vibrates.

 Take care when working with fire.

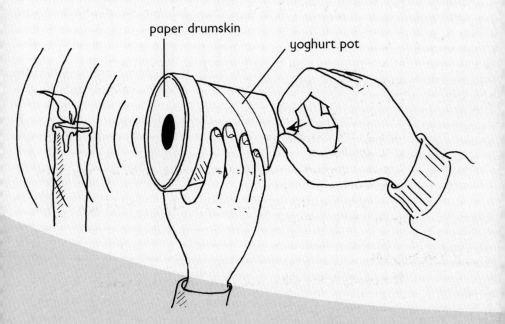

paper drumskin

yoghurt pot

Curriculum links

KS2 Sc4 3e,g. QCA SoW 5F Changing sounds
Envtl St/Science/E&F/PUE/Level E/Target 5

Scottish referencing key

Environmental Studies (Envtl St): Science	
ATTAINMENT OUTCOMES	SKILLS STRANDS
Earth and space (E&S)	Earth in space (ES) Materials from earth (ME) Changing materials (CM)
Energy and forces (E&F)	Properties and uses of energy (PUE) Conversion and transfer of energy (CTE) Forces and their effect (FTE)
Living things and the processes of life (LT&PL)	Variety and characteristic features (VCF) The processes of life (PL) Interaction of living things with their environment (ILTTE)
Health Education (Health Ed)	
ATTAINMENT OUTCOMES	SKILLS STRANDS
Taking responsibility for health (TRH)	Physical health (PH)